The Story of the Twir

A folktale from India

Writer: Helen Bradford, Ph.D.

Illustrator: Adeeba

Mathematical stories from historic Cambridge

CAMathories™ Books

CAMathories™ Folktale Mathematics™ Series
Supporting Diversity and Inclusion for One World
Curriculum for 3-4 years old
Series 2: Keeping Count 1 to 5
(Folktales from India, Ghana, and Ukraine)

Published by CAMathories Company
55 Union Place, #238, Summit, NJ 07901, U.S.A.
USA | UK | China
www.camathories.com

ISBN: 979-8-9867992-1-6

Editor-in-Chief: Kit Cheung, Ph.D. (Cantab)
Editor: Monika Gupta
Typesetter and Proofreader: Bookone Graphics

Once upon a time there were two sisters called Haldi and Adarak. They had five gifts for their grandparents, but only Haldi was happy to walk all the way to take the gifts safely to her grandparents' village. Her journey is filled with all kinds of surprises along the way... Enjoy learning to count to five as Haldi goes on her journey, and wonder what her grandmother gives her to bring home!

Once upon a time there were two sisters called Haldi and Adarak. In Hindi, the language that people from India speak, Haldi means turmeric, and Adarak means ginger. They are both the names of spices, as we have just discovered. The sisters were twins. This means they had been born together. They shared the same birthday each year.

One day, Haldi suggested to Adarak that they visit their grandparents. "We haven't seen them for so long," said Haldi. "We could take them some gifts." "You go," said Adarak, grumpily. "They live so far away. I will stay here and go another time."

So Haldi wrapped five gifts for her grandparents. She wrapped each gift in brown paper to make one, two, three, four, five parcels. She could not find a basket to put them in, so she tucked them under her arm, and began the long journey to her grandparents' home. What do you think the gift inside each parcel is?

Along the way, she came upon an oven, full of baking loaves. "Little girl! Little girl!" called out the loaves. "Please take us out of here! Do take us out or we shall be burnt!" Now Haldi was a kind, thoughtful girl. She stopped, carefully put down her five parcels one at a time and took out all the loaves of bread from the oven.

"Thank you," sighed the five loaves. "That feels much better."

"Your're welcome," said Haldi.

She counted the loaves, one, two, three, four, five. Then she picked up her parcels, one, two, three, four, five, and went on her way.

After a time, Haldi passed a cow lowing beside five empty milk pails, and the cow said to her: "Little girl! Little girl! No one has come to milk me today. Please milk me! Please!"

So, because we now know how kind Haldi is, she stopped, carefully put down her five parcels, one at a time, and milked the cow.

"Thank you," said the cow. "That feels much better."

"You're welcome," said Haldi.

A little while later, Haldi walked past an apple tree with branches so full of ripe apples that they were pulling the tree over.

"Little girl! Little girl! Please shake my branches. There are so many apples, I cannot stand up straight!"

What do you think Haldi did? Well, I'll tell you. She stopped and she smiled at the tree. She carefully put down her five parcels, one at a time, and she gave the tree a good shake. One, two, three, four, five apples tumbled to the ground.

"Thank you," sighed the tree, relieved. "That feels much better."

"You're welcome!" replied Haldi.

She counted the fallen apples, one, two, three, four, five. Then she picked up her parcels, one, two, three, four, five, and went on her way.

At last, Haldi reached her grandparents' home. They were pleased to see her and hugged her tightly. So tight in fact that all her parcels tumbled, one, two, three, four, five, all over the floor! Oh dear! Haldi calmly picked the parcels up one by one, and gave them to her grandparents.

They opened their gifts; inside each parcel was a jar of spice for cooking delicious meals with.

Haldi helped her grandmother in the kitchen, and together they used the one, two, three, four, five spices to make the best-tasting curry ever.

After their meal, Haldi said goodbye to her grandparents and began the long walk home.

In return for her kindness, her grandparents gave her five presents, each one wrapped carefully and placed in a basket. How much easier would it be now to carry them home! No more dropping them and picking them up again.

"These are for you," her grandmother whispered to her as she hugged her goodbye.

When Haldi arrived back home, her sister Adarak came running out to greet her.

"Presents!" she squealed when she saw Haldi's basket.

"Yes, grandmother gave them to me."

"All of them?" Adarak asked.

"All one, two, three, four, five of them," said Haldi as she counted them one by one.

"What about me?" said Adarak, ungraciously.

"I asked you to come with me, but you didn't want to."

Haldi opened her gifts. She laid out each one in front of her: a glittering sliver bangle; a cool cotton scarf; a bowl and a spoon carved from wood so that she could mix her own spices. Her last gift, what could it be?

About the Writer
Helen Bradford, Ph.D.

Dr. Helen Bradford is a passionate lifelong early years educator who has published widely over her career. She has worked in the early years for almost 30 years, where her specialist area of expertise is developing childhood language and literacy 0-8 years. She worked at the Faculty of Education at the University of Cambridge between 2003 to 2015, where she led literacy on the Early Years and Primary PGCE course, alongside Mrs. Penny Coltman, currently, the Early Years Education Mentor at CAMathories™, and Dr. David Whitebread, the late Founding Chief Education Officer at CAMathories™.

Dr. Bradford gained her Master's degree entitled 'The Perceptions of Three- and Four-Year-Old Children as Writers' from the University of Cambridge in 2007, receiving a top 'A' grade for her research. Helen moved to UCL (University College London) Institute of Education in 2015, where she lectured for four years across early childhood Master's courses, working with diverse cohorts of students from across the globe. Her Ph.D. research, entitled 'Co-Constructing Writing Pedagogy with Two-and-Three-Year-Old Children', won the 2019 United Kingdom Literacy Association prize for best thesis.

Dr. Bradford is the Early Years Language and Literacy Mentor and an Education Team Member of CAMathories, alongside Dr. Lorna Ayton (Mathematics Advisor) and Mrs. Coltman (Early Years Education Mentor for Mathematics and Science). Dr. Bradford advises on age-appropriate literacy and language contexts across the early year's learning resources for CAMathories™.

About the Peer-reviewer
Lorna Ayton, Ph.D. (Cantab)

Dr. Lorna Ayton is a lifetime mathematician. She was admitted to the University of Cambridge to study B.A. Mathematics (First Class Honors), followed by Part III Mathematics (Distinction), and then a Ph.D. in Mathematics. Dr. Ayton's Ph.D. thesis is awarded "The Outstanding Thesis Prize" by Springer. Dr. Ayton is a researcher in the Department of Applied Mathematics and Theoretical Physics in the Waves research group at the University of Cambridge. She also teaches mathematics to students in a local secondary school. Dr. Ayton is a co-founder and Mathematics Advisor of CAMathories Company and a member of the Education Team that designs the curriculum for CAMathories™. Dr. Ayton ensures that mathematics is well-applied in our games and that learning mathematics can be fun and rewarding!

About the Peer-reviewer
Penny Coltman, MEd. Res. (Cantab)

Mrs. Penny Coltman is an experienced educator and trainer of teachers in the early years education sector in the United Kingdom. She gained her M.Ed. Res. at the University of Cambridge. Mrs. Coltman was a manager and lecturer on the University of Cambridge's Early Years and Primary PGCE course for 20+ years. In 2007, Mrs. Coltman was awarded a prestigious Pilkington Prize by the University of Cambridge in recognition of her contributions to the Early Years Teachers' Education.

Mrs. Coltman specializes in early mathematics and science education and collaborated with Dr. David Whitebread (1948-2021) in researching self-regulation and the role of language in supporting early learning. She has worked with several educational publishers, including, BBC worldwide, and created two award-winning practical classroom resources to support the teaching of early mathematics. Mrs. Coltman recently retired from the Faculty of Education at the University of Cambridge. Currently, she is the Early Years Education Mentor for CAMathories™ and a member of CAMathories' Education Team that designs the curriculum for CAMathories™ with Dr. Lorna Ayton.

About the Editor-in-Chief
Kit Cheung, Ph.D. (Cantab)

Dr. Kit Cheung has lived, studied, and worked in different places, from the fun yet hustle and bustle cities of Hong Kong (China) and Singapore, to the awesome Royal Mile in Edinburgh, Scotland, then to fairytale-like Cambridge in England, and later to Baltimore, the crab cake capital of the world, before settling in the garden state, New Jersey, of the U.S.A. Dr. Cheung likes to travel to different places in Asia, Europe, and Australasia, to meet different people, to learn about different cultures, and is fascinated by different folk stories from different areas. Dr. Cheung is a recipient of the Chevening Scholarship (awarded by the British Foreign, Commonwealth and Development Office, U.K.) and Cambridge Overseas Trust (by the University of Cambridge, U.K.), and has obtained a Ph.D. degree from the School of Humanities and Social Sciences at the University of Cambridge. Dr. Cheung is a co-founder and the Chief Executive Officer of CAMathories Company.

Dr. David Whitebread
Ph.D. (1948-2021)

Dr. David Whitebread had been the Acting Director (External Relations), Centre for Research on Play in Education, Development, and Learning (PEDAL), in the Faculty of Education, University of Cambridge. Dr. Whitebread was one of the first members of the Faculty of Education when it was founded. He had more than 30 years of research experience in children learning through play. Dr. Whitebread was also a consultant advising many educational institutions in different parts of the world to improve their early childhood learning programs. Every year, PEDAL Research Centre at the University of Cambridge hosts a David Whitebread Memorial Lecture to commemorate the contribution of Dr. Whitebread to early years education.

Dr. Whitebread was a co-founder and the founding Chief Education Officer of CAMathories Company. Dr. Whitebread advised the pedagogy and curriculum for CAMathories™. He also wrote stories and games with Mrs. Penny Coltman (CAMathories' Mentor for Early Years Education) for CAMathories™.

Other books published by CAMathories™

CAMathories Company has published a series of story books that is part of a comprehensive CAMathories™ Folktale Mathematics™ curriculum that teaches mathematics in an enjoyable and engaging way using folktales from various parts of the world. CAMathories™ Folktale Mathematics™ offers a research-informed approach to traditional mathematics classroom pedagogy and at the same time supports diversity and inclusion for one world.

"The Story of the Twin Sisters" is the first book in the second series of the CAMathories™ Folktale Mathematics™ curriculum for children aged 3-4 years old. Series 2: Keeping Count 1 to 5. Two other books in the same series are: "The Story of the Leopard's Spots" (from Ghana, Africa), and "The Kind Fox and the Little Cat" (from Ukraine). This series helps readers to develop an awareness of the "stable order" principle – we always say the same numbers in the same, stable order. The Series also help students to further practice counting things that are not objects, such as actions or movement, and things that cannot be seen, for example, sounds.

"The Story of the Leopard's Spots" is a folktale from Ghana (a country in Africa) which tells the story of five animals having a jungle party. Readers will learn to count up to 5 as they follow the animals' celebrations and discover who has stolen their party food! The book will support children to learn to count actions and movements other than objects.

"The Kind Fox and the Little Cat" is a folktale from Ukraine. It tells the story of a fox and a cat who became good friends and scare off their animal neighbours who tried to trick them. Readers will have many opportunities to count out loud from one to five as they follow the story.

Other CAMathories™ Folktale Mathematics™ Series introduces children to interesting and enjoyable folktales from different cultures and teach fundamental mathematics at the same time. Series 1: Count and recite 1 to 5, includes: "Goldilocks and the Three Bears" (from Britain), "Paco and the Giant Chili Plant" (from Mexico) and "5 Little Monkeys Catching the Moon" (from China).

CAMathories™ Folktale Mathematics™ Series

Supporting Diversity and Inclusion for One World

Curriculum for 3-4 years old

Series 2: Keeping Count 1 to 5

(Folktales from India, Ghana, and Ukraine)

To learn more about the research and conceptual

approaches behind Folktale Mathemeatics™

Please visit

www.camathories.com

.

9 798986 799216